Him & Them

Workbook

Don Middleton, D.O.

Dedication

"Just be the best you that you can be today."

The best advice my sponsor Jim D. ever gave me.
You saved my bacon Jimmy – thank you.

Introduction

There are a lot of tools in your tool box to help you overcome your addiction. This workbook is one of them. It is designed to work along with the Him & Them book and works best that way rather than as a stand-alone item used on its own. The book obviously has a great deal more information and takes the time to discuss many topics that may not be fully investigated in these pages. The ideal situation would be for you to read the first few chapters in the book and discuss them or even re-read them one at a time with your Recovery Partner (RP). Then start the step work, and work the pages here. The two of you can go over the answers carefully.

There will be a chapter for every step. Many of the chapters, especially the early ones, will also have a component of Relapse Prevention Planning (RPP) which is discussed in chapter 17 of the book, and is found in the back of this workbook. Relapse prevention has decades of thought as well as trial and error behind it. There are many well-considered papers written about the planning, and it has become a standard component of treatment. The truth is though, that almost no 12-step programs pay any attention to this vital tool. Often, it is considered a tertiary part of treatment, but Him & Them wishes to give more importance to it, and will always consider RPP as indispensable.

Frequently, relapse prevention planning is done with a professional counselor, and some of them have a great deal of experience with it. If your recovery has professional counseling as a component, then you would be wise to use some of the time to get their input on making a solid plan, and adding their insight to where you might be lacking in your plan. We are, however, trying to make this program a stand-alone tool, and hope that it will serve those who cannot obtain professional input.

Regardless if you do relapse prevention planning with your recovery partner or a psychologist, (or both!) take it very seriously. Relapse is a part of some people's story, but it doesn't have to be part of yours. Far too many people with an addiction die as a result of relapse. This is literally a life or death undertaking and should be approached that way. We are a lighthearted group, but relapse is serious stuff. Far too many of us die in our disease.

Get a bible that speaks to your heart. Many try to be exact translations, and others which use paraphrasing in order to be more available in common language. If you want a recommendation, Him & Them currently recommends *"The Life Recovery Bible - Second Edition"* by Tyndale House Publishers, which is aimed at people trying to surrender their addiction to God. It uses the popular New Living Translation which is generally considered to be accurate. This leans more toward the thought-for-thought translation rather than the word-for-word type of translation like the NIV uses. Some people consider the NIV translation as more *"accurate"* for deep-dive Bible study.

Him & Them won't be pulled into the rabbit hole of arguing different translations, any more than it wishes to debate the differences between Christian denominations. Their traditions, rituals, and theology belong to them. Things that clearly conflict with the

Word of God should be questioned by someone, but Him & Them is busy walking people away from their addictions. It is our opinion that almost anything that gets a person into prayerfully considering God's Word is a good thing.

The basic structure is this: Read the chapter. Then, 4-5 days a week there will be a verse or two to read, pray over, and meditate on. Try to let God open your eyes and heart to how His Word applies to your particular situation. Then a couple of questions to think about and write answers to. If you need to, get an extra notebook or journal so your answers aren't limited to the space given. Let your heart soar, and write as much as you need. There can't be too much written, only not enough. Finally, discuss your thoughts with your RP weekly. That, of course, is the ideal - life happens, so be flexible.

Spend time daily in prayer and meditation, clearing your mind to be open to the Truth. Ask frequently for God to open your eyes and ears to His Truth and how it applies to your life. Try earnestly to make time daily in God's Word. Even just a few verses or a chapter a day can be life-changing. Perhaps you might also use an app that sends you a daily verse. If you are anything like hundreds of millions of other Christians, the specific questions that you have will eventually be answered in this manner. Often sooner than you expect.

We pray that those who might pick at nits and fight over academic points will prayerfully consider the unintended consequences of their actions. While they may be for very sincere, not at all ego-centered reasons, they could have the outcome of driving a person away from a program that could save their very life, and allow them the freedom to reunite with their Creator. Please remember this is a life or death situation before you take away another's hope for healing in an effort to prove to everyone how very smart you are.

It is the position of Him & Them that anything that helps loosen the chains of addiction is a good thing. Even if it doesn't exactly match our individual understanding of theology, know this: Nobody is going to be reunited with God when they are in their active addiction. Getting free is the first step in walking back into the loving relationship that God intended us to have in Christ. God has whispered this program into being, let it be. Remember Luke 6:41-42.

If this doesn't match your particular personal philosophy, feel free to stop reading now. You will, of course, be guilty of something that has kept millions of addicts addicted: Contempt before investigation. So, move away from the debate podium or your flame-ready keyboard, close the door to a private place, and hit your knees. Reach out to the God of all creation even if you have doubts. That's Ok. There is more waiting for you regardless of what you think your past might dictate. Just quit fighting and surrender.

"Seek first His kingdom and His righteousness, and all these things will be given to you as well." Matthew 6:33

Workbook: Step 1

"We admitted that we were powerless over our use of substances or behaviors - and that our lives had become unmanageable."

The confusion between admitting powerlessness and being helpless seems never-ending when our ego is in control. Our demanding ego wishes to reign over its own kingdom as its own god. Don't be ashamed, this desire, even if hidden behind religious rituals, is a pretty universal thought – *"I am in control of everything in my life"*.

Before we get started on step one, there's only one question to ask yourself: *"How's that been working for me?"*

Right. Same here.

Let's get started.

Day 1:

• Look up definitions of both *"powerless"* and *"unmanageable"* and write them down.

_____

_____

_____

_____

_____

_____

_____

_____

It is assumed that you agree there is no person ever that has God's power over the entire universe. Admitting powerlessness seems difficult to many, but it is actually as simple as that. No one has all power, except God. That means that we all have things we are powerless to do.

• Without listing your addiction, list 5 things that you are powerless to do.

Example: *I am not able to be a winning Super Bowl quarterback* (if you are, good on you. Pick something else)

1. _____

2. _____

3. _____

4. _____

5. _____

That wasn't so painful, was it? All of us have things we will never have power over.

• Write a few sentences of what someone who knows you well would say to describe your recent life.

_____
_____
_____
_____
_____
_____
_____
_____
_____

• Think of your life today and list the things that aren't working out according to your plan. No excuses, no blame, just the list.

_____
_____
_____
_____
_____
_____
_____
_____
_____
_____

• Look up Jeremiah 29:11 and read it out loud to yourself slowly a couple of times. Journal how it affects you emotionally.

_____
_____
_____
_____
_____
_____
_____

Day 2:

• Losing control isn't on anyone's plan. What does losing control feel like to you emotionally, and if you can, physically?

_____
_____
_____
_____
_____
_____

• Give a few examples of when loss of control happened to you, and what you did to try to regain control of the situation.

_____
_____
_____
_____
_____
_____
_____
_____

• What kind of trouble has your use led to? Legal, Domestic, Work? Come on - get honest here.

_____
_____
_____
_____
_____
_____
_____

• Tell about a situation where it was obvious to everyone that you had lost control over your drug of choice (DOC). Include the feelings and emotions surrounding that situation.

_____
_____
_____
_____
_____

• Finish this sentence. *"Aside from my addiction, the real problem in my life is* _____
_____
_____
_____
_____."

Read Matthew 18:1-4 and write about how you think this relates to you overcoming addiction.

_____

_____

_____

_____

_____

_____

Day 3:

Too often trying to quit is like walking through deep mud. We struggle, and fight, but the harder we try, the deeper we seem to sink. No, it isn't just you, very few people quit for good on their first try. Those who stop trying, die from their disease after a miserable life. There is another way – carry on. We've got your six.

• Describe various times you have attempted to quit or modify your use. Specifically list the plans you have made and what the results were.

_____

_____

_____

_____

_____

• What areas in your life are out of control because of your use? What have you done to "manage" them and how did that work out?

_____

_____

_____

_____

_____

_____

_____

_____

• What would a list of how your behavior affects your family and friends look like?

_____

_____

_____

_____

_____

_____

• Write a gratitude list with as many things on it as you can think of. Quietly thank God for each of these things as often as possible – daily if you can.

The last page of this workbook has room for a gratitude list so you can find it easily every day throughout this season in your life. Accept the challenge to pray over it every day for a month. But be careful! You might just find yourself being transformed by the renewing of your mind!

• Now go back and write more on all of these things – something tells us that you are not being completely open to the whole truth. Yet.

• Read 2 Corinthians 5:17 a few times, and sit with it for a while. What about old you will you miss the least?

_____

_____

_____

_____

_____

_____

_____

_____

_____

_____

_____

Day 4:

Relapse Prevention Planning

• Get some notebook paper and write a "*Dear John*" break-up letter to your drug of choice, and let it know exactly how you feel right now. Be very specific and as graphic as you need to be about how it has affected your health, relationships, career, and especially your walk with God. Go long and detailed on this, it may be a tool that saves you from relapse in the future. No need for fancy religious words if they aren't part of your daily vocabulary, it's not like this will go in the church newsletter. This is between you and your DOC. This will not be published anywhere, so be honest and raw.

Some people ceremoniously burn this letter, but others keep it stashed - maybe even with your RP (if it is too incriminating). Then it can be re-read some day when you need an extra dose of motivation to stay sober. We tend to forget how bad things got. It's kinda' part of the disease.

Workbook Step 2

"We came to believe that our Heavenly Father could and would restore us to sanity."

God has a plan for you and it isn't to be miserable and addicted. Millions of pages have been written on the meaning of life and how we are supposed to live as good humans. The truth is far simpler. Ask God for his will in your life, and quit fighting it when it occurs.

"For I know the plans I have for you," declares the Lord, "plans to prosper you and not to harm you, plans to give you hope and a future."

Jeremiah 29:11

Day 1:

• Just for fun, see if you can recognize some insane thinking in other people that you know.

_____
_____
_____
_____
_____
_____
_____
_____

• After reading about the definitions of insanity, list some *"less than sane"* decisions you have made.

_____
_____
_____

_____
_____
_____
_____
_____
_____
_____

• Do you have fears surrounding the word insane?

_____
_____
_____
_____
_____

• Try to visualize sanity and how it might feel. See if you can describe it in words.

_____
_____
_____
_____
_____
_____
_____
_____
_____

• Read and ponder Romans 7:18-20. Write about how it fits your situation.

_____
_____
_____
_____
_____
_____
_____
_____

Day 2:

• Describe a time when you let go of a fear. How did it happen and what were the results?

_____

_____

_____

_____

_____

_____

_____

_____

• Do you have difficulty in believing things that cannot be seen or proved by science? Explain. It's really ok to be honest here.

_____

_____

_____

_____

_____

_____

_____

• Have you ever been hurt by someone who said they were deeply religious?

_____

_____

_____

_____

_____

_____

_____

_____

• Review your gratitude list and add any new things that come to mind.

• Look up Romans 3:23. Slowly think about it as you do mindful, meditative breathing. Allow it to sink in, and then journal any feelings or emotions it brings out in you.

_____

_____

_____

_____

_____

_____

_____

_____

_____

Day 3:

• Honestly discuss any concerns that God can heal your addiction.

_____

_____

_____

_____

_____

_____

_____

_____

• Write your feelings about the phrase *"Let go, and Let God."* (Oh, and quit trying to be fancy and impressing your RP with big words. Get real!)

_____

_____

_____

_____

_____

_____

_____

_____

_____

• Tell of a time or two when God intervened in your life. If you can't think of an incident in your life, how about someone else's?

_____
_____
_____
_____
_____
_____
_____
_____
_____
_____

• Read and contemplate John 14:6 journal how it feels in your heart to own that verse.

_____
_____
_____
_____
_____
_____
_____
_____
_____

Day 4:

Relapse Prevention Plan

• Write out detailed memory of the last time you quit and then relapsed. There is room for this in the back of the workbook. Include where you were, who you were with, and what stressors were going on at the time. Spend time trying to remember the emotions, feelings, and especially the negativity that came before the first use. Be very complete; come back later and fill in details.

• After you are done with the last relapse, try your best to remember, if you can, the relapse before that and do this exercise for it too. This can be a lot of difficult work and even dredge up a lot of bad feelings, but it is a huge help to keeping sober.

Do it!

Workbook Step 3

*"Made a decision to turn our will and our lives
over to the care of God"*

In life, surrender is scary. In addiction, not surrendering can be fatal. The number of people that die every day from addiction is heartbreaking. Especially to those who have escaped and know that the path is simple. Not easy, but definitely simple. Jesus promises a light yolk, and compared to the weight of a life in addiction, it is. Drop the heavy stone hanging from your neck and take the easier way. Absolutely everyone that does is grateful for the decision – however hard the path might be to get there.

Day 1:

• Who is God to you? Whatever your initial thought is, expand it for clarity.

_____

_____

_____

_____

_____

_____

_____

• Who are you in relation to God? Expand on that with a paragraph or so.

_____

_____

_____

_____

_____
_____
_____
_____
_____
_____

• Who is Jesus to you and how does he fit into this relationship?

_____
_____
_____
_____
_____
_____
_____
_____

• Read 1 John 4:1-21 and Then go back through these questions again. Has this chapter changed anything for you?

_____
_____
_____
_____
_____
_____

Day 2:

• What thoughts or fears surround the word "surrender" to you?

_____
_____
_____
_____
_____
_____

• Discuss a time when you actually surrendered. How well were you able to follow through with it?

_____

_____

_____

_____

_____

_____

• Discuss several times when someone in authority above you let you down.

_____

_____

_____

_____

_____

_____

• What does faith mean to you and what role does it have in your life?

_____

_____

_____

_____

_____

_____

_____

• Hebrews 11:6 has a message for you to ponder today. Journal about it and then try discussing it with a friend.

_____

_____

_____

_____

_____

_____

_____

_____

Day 3:

• What does it mean to you to turn your will over to God?

_____

_____

_____

_____

_____

_____

_____

• What does it mean to turn your life over to God?

_____

_____

_____

_____

_____

_____

_____

• Do you really, in your heart trust God to take over control of your life? Discuss any fears surrounding this.

_____

_____

_____

_____

_____

_____

_____

_____

_____

• Meditate over the verse in Jeremiah 29:11. Hold it in your heart. Journal your thoughts:

_____

_____

_____

_____

_____

_____

_____

_____

_____

_____

_____

_____

_____

Relapse Prevention

• Review the work you did last week, and make any needed changes or additions.

• Make a list of triggers. Those are people, places, or things that might "*trigger*" you into thinking about using your DOC. Then, write a possible "*alternative action*" or something you can do to walk past the trigger.

Example:

Trigger: *when I see the alcohol at circle K when I'm getting my morning coffee.*
Alternative action: *make my coffee at home.*

Some other examples might be: Being home alone, passing by a dealer's house, listening to specific music, hanging out with certain friends, a particular smell, going to a convenience store with liquor for sale. Specific concerts, holidays, vacations, hard day at work …There is potentially a zillion. Be thoughtful. Be thorough.

• Go to 1 Corinthians 10:13 and memorize it. Seriously. Memorize it.

Try this prayer on for size:

My Father,

Thank you for your love today and every day. I am so very grateful for the many blessings that you give me day after day. I am especially grateful for my sobriety, because I know it comes from you. God, I wish to live a life that serves your will. Replace my plans with your plans. Take away my selfish thoughts and replace them with a life filled with love for you and the rest of your children. Let me walk in Christ with your Son, serving your will in all I do.

Amen.

Workbook Step 4

"We made a searching and fearless moral inventory of ourselves."

This week you already have a lot of soul searching and writing to do, so we'll not add to it, but instead will offer verses to meditate on, and a few reminders to help you dig through the closet and get out all the inventory items. Do not skimp on this step. Many people that relapse, look back on a poorly done step 4.

God calls us to a life of accountability, and that translates into honesty with others and to yourself. Maybe honesty hasn't been your superpower up till now, but try it on for size. It only stings a little, and only at first. Honestly.

Day 1:

• Start today with this verse: John 8:32 and ask God to open your heart to the Truth.

• Get yourself alone and start writing all the things that you have remembered that you resent - times when others have hurt you. Try to make it in chronological order when possible, but don't let ANY excuses creep in. Satan will not like the fact that you are clearing up the clutter to let more God in, and will try to give you reasons to avoid the work. Don't bite the apple!

• Get a little exercise every day this week. Even a brisk walk around the block helps get the blood pumping and the mind working at its best!

Day 2:

• Proverbs 10:9 is today's verse to meditate over. Read it several times asking God for honesty to be a value above all else.

• Go back through and list all the times that you have hurt others. This is no time for shame or embarrassment. Don't play the blame game to yourself or to others. If you feel uncomfortable, that is probably a good thing because the stuff we need to clear out usually IS unpleasant. Don't veer away from the pain – lean into it. You don't have to be alone. Call a trusted someone to air out some of the feelings you are experiencing.

Our secrets keep us sick!

Day 3:

• Time to dig deeper today. Remember this is just writing things down, just taking the inventory. You are not doing anything with it, so if you have really done step 3 and given yourself to the Lord, then know that honesty in all things matters to Him.

• Today double down on making sure that all romantic and/or sexual relationships are addressed. It doesn't matter if they were long term or short encounters, almost all have resentments and hurt feelings associated with them. Write them down and do not skimp!

• Matthew 7:12 is today's verse – the Golden rule. Ask God to make it your new way of living. Meditate and repeat it slowly as you mindfully monitor your breathing. There is no goal. Just be alone with God's Word.

Day 4:

• Your verse today reminds you that you are New in Christ. This can be the greatest news of your life. The old you is an addict. The new

you does not need anything other than Christ to get through even the toughest of days. The person you used to be will use again. Shed that old you for the new Child of God you that is comfortable in sobriety.
• Meditate on 2 Corinthians 5:17

• Take a walk, jog, or a quick bike ride. Now, go over your inventory again. Ask God to open your heart to anything that you may be denying or unintentionally leaving out (not that you would do that- but we've heard other people have).

Be bold. Be courageous.

Workbook Step 5

"We admitted to God, to ourselves, and to another human being the exact nature of our wrongs."

In 2 Timothy 1:6-7, we are reminded that we have been given *"a spirit of power, love, and self-control."* This can give us comfort that we are designed to do the tough stuff which lets us work away at the biology that has been conspiring to keep us craving. Like walking across a huge, snow-drifted field, simply continuing to put one foot in front of the other, and eventually, you emerge on the other side. It wasn't necessarily easy, but it wasn't complicated either. Persistence pays off in all that we do. So be persistent and keep moving forward.

Day 1:

• What kinds of thoughts or fears does the word "confession" bring up to you?

_____

_____

_____

_____

_____

_____

• Discuss a time where a secret was shared that hurt you. Then discuss a time when you shared something that you shouldn't have.

_____

_____

_____

_____

_____

_____

_____

_____

_____

• Talk out on paper why *"Let bygones be bygones."* is a bad idea
when it comes to things that you have done wrong or that have been
done to you?

_____

_____

_____

_____

_____

_____

_____

_____

_____

_____

• Read and journal on Luke 8:17 and James 5:6. Try to see and
journal their wisdom in your life.

_____

_____

_____

_____

_____

_____

_____

_____

_____

_____

_____

_____

_____

Day 2:

• Discuss why it seems that we want to look good in others' eyes.

_____

_____

_____

_____

_____

_____

_____

_____

• Why is it important to confess to God and ourselves too? Don't we both already know all this stuff?

_____

_____

_____

_____

_____

_____

_____

_____

• If we all agree that honesty is the best policy, for what reason could we possibly want to withhold the truth from our RP, or ourselves, or God?

_____

_____

_____

_____

_____

_____

_____

_____

_____

• Read Psalm 32:1-5 and think about how it applies to you. Journal your thoughts.

_____

_____

_____

_____

_____

_____

_____

Day 3:

• Why do you suppose it is important to state the "*exact nature*" of our wrongs rather than a general idea of what we did?

_____

_____

_____

_____

_____

_____

_____

_____

• Try and make a guess at what happens if we leave the worst and most embarrassing thing out?

_____

_____

_____

_____

_____

_____

_____

_____

• Define "*humility*" and discuss how it could affect your life.

_____

_____

_____

_____

_____

_____

_____

_____

_____

• Do you think perfection is desirable? Achievable? How does the Bible discuss this?

_____

_____

_____

_____

_____

_____

_____

_____

_____

• Read and ponder Ecclesiastes 7:20 and 1 John 4:12. Write down your thoughts about these verses.

_____

_____

_____

_____

_____

_____

_____

_____

_____

Day 4:

Too often we look at confession as a punishment, but what we find as we walk away from the bonds of addiction is that the secrets we desire to keep are actually the punishment. We are designed to connect with each other, and our ego's efforts to stay secretive is a prison cell of our own design.

Paul told us over and over to "*repent and turn to God*" promising that the Lord is waiting to accept us back fully restored and blameless. The first step in repentance is clearing out the old garbage to make room for the new treasure. Confession does this.

• As you prepare to do step 5 with your RP, meditate on these two verses, given to you by God, perhaps for this very moment.

1 John 1:9

Acts 3:19

Workbook Step 6

*"We became entirely ready to have God remove
all our unhelpful habits that separate us from
Him and others."*

As we allow God to trade out our false self for our True self, new in Christ, fears frequently arise as the ego strives to keep control over us. This battle is as old as humans (read the garden of Eden story), and universal. The good news is told to us by Jesus over and over. Last is first, lowest is highest, let go to gain. Die to be reborn.

This step demands that we develop patience for God's timeline, and increased willingness to continue letting go. Neither comes naturally, and neither soothes our ego, so they both make us uncomfortable. When you feel uncomfortable, it might just be the Spirit letting you know you may be on the right track.

Suck it up, and keep moving forward. You've got this!

Day 1:

Define "*unhelpful habits*" and any thoughts or fears surrounding the use of those words with regard to you personally.

_____

_____

_____

_____

_____

_____

_____

_____

_____

• Spend time asking God to open your eyes and heart to the truth, and make an initial list of your unhelpful habits.

_____

_____

_____

_____

_____

_____

_____

_____

_____

_____

_____

_____

_____

_____

_____

• Mindfully read and journal your thoughts around Ephesians 4:2

_____

_____

_____

_____

_____

_____

_____

Day 2:

• Are there things on your list of unhelpful habits that you secretly (or not so secretly) enjoy and/or wish to keep?

_____

_____

_____

_____

_____

_____

_____

• Is there a part of you that worries that changing all these things might mean that you would no longer be you? Expand on the answer.

_____

_____

_____

_____

_____

_____

_____

_____

_____

• Is there something that you think cannot be changed? Why?

_____

_____

_____

_____

_____

_____

_____

• Do you really believe in your heart that you can be completely changed?

_____

_____

_____

_____

_____

_____

_____

• Read Jeremiah 29:11-14 slowly, and meditate on it. Journal how it applies to your life and specifically to step 6.

_____

_____

_____

_____
_____
_____
_____
_____

Day 3:

• Google "*step 6 character defects*" and see if you find anything you should add to your list of unhelpful habits. Add them.

• Discuss what "*entirely ready*" means to you and specifically with regard to this step. Has procrastination been a part of your life (and should it be on your unhelpful habits list?)?

_____
_____
_____
_____
_____
_____
_____
_____
_____
_____
_____

• Write out Galatians 5:22-23 and a brief definition of each of the 9 "*Fruits of the Spirit*"

_____
_____
_____
_____
_____
_____
_____
_____
_____

_____

_____

_____

_____

_____

_____

Day 4:

Relapse prevention

• Review your relapse prevention plan so far. Look carefully for areas that need clarification or improvement.

• Study the Him & Them book section about "*Emotional Relapse*" in chapter 17, and write a couple of paragraphs about it. Note especially any of the emotions or feelings you have experienced in the past and what you could do if they arise again.

• Read Colossians 3:5-10 and discuss it with your RP.

_____

_____

_____

_____

_____

_____

_____

_____

_____

_____

_____

_____

_____

_____

Workbook Step 7

*"We humbly asked God to remove
our unhelpful habits."*

Step 7 seems to say *"I want to change everything about me."* That is, of course, just an exaggeration. Everyone, even those most deeply ingrained in their addiction, have some things worthy of keeping. God gifts us all not only with the Holy Spirit, but also with other spiritual gifts like service, discernment, teaching, leadership… etc. These are things that we should not only keep, but also tap into to move forward in our Christian walk.

Day 1:

• Write a list of Godly habits that you do have, and wish to keep or improve.

_____

_____

_____

_____

_____

_____

_____

_____

_____

_____

• Look at your Step 6 list of unhelpful habits, and after each one, write a replacement Fruit of the Spirit. There's no right or wrong here, but until we thoughtfully consider it and write it down, we are just engaging in fanciful thought.

_____
_____
_____
_____
_____
_____
_____
_____
_____
_____
_____

• Discuss the difference between *"surrender"* and *"compliance"*. Which seems more like you in the past? Which is step 7 asking for?

_____
_____
_____
_____
_____
_____
_____
_____

• How, if any, has your understanding of God's ability to transform you changed?

_____
_____
_____
_____
_____
_____
_____
_____
_____
_____

• Pray on the verses of Psalm 139:23-24. Let them enter into your heart forever. Jot down any thoughts that come to you during this meditation of God's Word.

_____

_____

_____

_____

_____

_____

_____

_____

_____

Day 2:

• Why do you suppose that humility is so hard for humans?

_____

_____

_____

_____

_____

_____

_____

_____

• Tell about a time you tried to form a new habit and failed. What happened?

_____

_____

_____

_____

_____

_____

_____

_____

• How has your daily prayer and meditation habit developed? What could you do to make it more regular? More effective?

_____
_____
_____
_____
_____
_____
_____
_____
_____
_____

• Review your gratitude list. Are there things that you should add to remember in your prayer life? Add them there, but there is room here to discuss any thoughts you have on the changes.

_____
_____
_____
_____
_____
_____
_____
_____

• Look up Mark 11:22-24 and journal about it after some time meditating on its words.

_____
_____
_____
_____
_____
_____
_____
_____
_____

Day 3:

• Meditate a bit, and then journal what life might look like without the top three things on your unhelpful habits list.

_____

_____

_____

_____

_____

_____

_____

_____

_____

_____

_____

_____

_____

_____

• Take those top three items that you feel most need God's attention and start praying them away. If you have difficulty ranking them, discuss it with your RP.

• Use a prayer like this and insert your top three, one at a time:

> *Father, I humbly come to you today to ask for your healing grace. I know that _____ has been a problem in my life, and the way I interact with others. I feel convicted that I still act that way. If it is your will, please take it from me, and let me see your children through your eyes. In Jesus' name, I pray. Amen.*

Say this prayer every day with these top three identified unhelpful habits. It may be weeks or even months, but God will remove them in His time.

Day 4:

Relapse Prevention

Warning! Do not let your guard down and cut corners on re-lapse planning. That's like driving without your seatbelt. You can do it, but it is risky. It's well known that people who work these plans experience longer and higher quality sobriety.

• Look up "*Mental Relapse*", and study what it means with regard to addiction relapse.

• Make a list of thoughts that were bothering you before your last couple of relapses. Consider their reality or lack thereof, and decide what kinds of things could be done in response to these popping up again. Discuss in with your RP.

Workbook Step 8

"We made a list of all persons we had harmed, and became willing to make amends to them all."

What? Another list?!?

Yes, and the good news is that is all this step asks for – just a list, so release the breath you are holding in, and relax a bit. In this step we stop looking exclusively inward and start to consider the others that we've left hurt in our wake. Once again, as if it needs to be said, honesty is key. The one thing that you leave off may be the very thing that beats you up mentally and emotionally, so be thorough.

We demand forgiveness, but we are so stingy in giving it out. God forgave you when you were still in your addiction and acting terribly. He wants us to act the same way to His children. Ephesians 4:31-32

You have come a long way, why get sloppy and do a half-hearted job now?

Day 1:

• Define the word *"willingness"*. Give examples when you weren't and when you were in the past.

_____

_____

_____

_____

_____

_____

• How would pride interfere with being willing complete this list?

_____

_____

_____

_____

_____

_____

_____

_____

• Name and discuss any fears or resentments that you have surrounding this activity.

_____

_____

_____

_____

_____

_____

_____

_____

• Read Proverbs 3:5-8 carefully, pray that God would give it importance in your heart, and journal your thoughts afterward.

_____

_____

_____

_____

_____

_____

_____

_____

_____

Day 2:

• Write the definition of "*responsibility*" and discuss how it has been important in your life.

_____
_____
_____
_____
_____
_____
_____
_____
_____
_____

• Do the same thing with the word "*defensiveness*".

_____
_____
_____
_____
_____
_____
_____
_____
_____

• Are there people that are due an amends that have also harmed you too? List them and write in detail both sides to discuss with your RP.

_____
_____
_____
_____
_____
_____
_____

_____

_____

_____

_____

_____

_____

_____

_____

_____

• Are there people that you are leaving off because you would owe them a lot of money that you would have difficulty repaying? Write them down in detail so you can at least share them with your RP.

_____

_____

_____

_____

_____

_____

_____

_____

_____

• 2 Corinthians 8:11-15 has a relevant message for today's work. Read it, ponder it.

_____

_____

_____

_____

_____

_____

_____

_____

_____

_____

Day 3:

• Write the definition of "*forgiveness*", and discuss why it might be important in your sobriety.

_____

_____

_____

_____

_____

_____

_____

_____

_____

• Go through the list of those you've harmed, and attach at least one of your unhealthy habits to each one of the actions. Pray that God relieves you of the bondage of that habit.

_____

_____

_____

_____

_____

_____

_____

_____

_____

• Work through the list of wrongs done to you, and pray that God would let you have a heart of forgiveness to each of them regardless of how bad they hurt you. Do this every day until you feel at peace with their transgression. Why is this important?

_____

_____

_____

_____

_____
_____
_____
_____
_____

• Read Matthew 6:12. Pray for understanding of the word "*as*"

Day 4:

• Review your list and pray that God opens your heart to any wrongs committed toward others that you are hiding or forgetting. Include them.

_____
_____
_____
_____
_____
_____
_____
_____

• In Exodus 21: 23-25, there is clearly a retribution kind of justice. Read Matthew 5:38-48. Why would Jesus change the rule?

_____
_____
_____
_____
_____
_____
_____
_____
_____

• Meditate on the quote "*Pain that isn't transformed, will surely be transferred.*" Journal what that means to your life.

_____

_____

_____

_____

_____

_____

_____

Day 5:

• Go to the RPP section and write about what "*physical relapse*" means to you. List specific actions that you must avoid to stay sober.

Workbook Step 9

"Made direct amends to such people, except when to do so would injure them or others."

So often, the person with an addiction has gone through hundreds of cycles of use, bad behavior, and apology. Again and again, it occurs until those closest to them are done hearing it. The words *"I'm really sorry"* come across as falsehoods even to those who understand the neurotransmitter/genetics/neuroplasticity transition which has occurred. It is just so painful to think that someone who is trusted and loved would seemingly lie over and over.

Being sorry is more about making ourselves feel less guilt. The point of step 9 is to instead focus our attention on the others, and actually take responsibility for our actions. Just because we suffered from a mental disease, doesn't relieve us of responsibility for our actions. But note - this action demands thought and nuance. Impulsivity or selfish carelessness can easily make bad worse, so the guidance of our Recovery Partner is more important here than anywhere else in the program.

The goal is the restoration of relationships if possible, resolution of old grievances, and when needed, restitution of any financial losses as is possible. The range of responses is wide, but out of your control. Sometimes it is advisable to discuss difficult Step 9 work with a psychologist or similar experienced professional. All you are responsible for is prayerfully treating the other person as the child of God that they are. Anything less will fall short of His desire for you. So move deliberately, and move in love.

But keep moving.

Day 1:

• Look up and write definitions for "*apology*" and "*amends*" discuss the difference.

_____
_____
_____
_____
_____
_____
_____
_____
_____

• Who are you least looking forward to making amends to? Why?

_____
_____
_____
_____
_____
_____
_____

• How does the concept of freedom come into play on this step?

_____
_____
_____
_____
_____
_____
_____
_____

• Matthew 5:9 talks about making peace with others. Lift this verse up frequently on your prayers this week.

Day 2:

• Discuss the difference between direct, indirect, and living amends.

_____

_____

_____

_____

_____

_____

_____

_____

• List anyone where you think making amends to them would cause harm. List the specific harm so you can discuss it with your RP.

_____

_____

_____

_____

_____

_____

_____

• List anybody that it may be impossible to make amends to. Why? What can be done instead to take responsibility for your actions?

_____

_____

_____

_____

_____

_____

_____

• Read Numbers 5:6-7. Journal your thoughts about the phrase "_unfaithful to the Lord_" (NIV)

_____

_____

_____

_____

_____

_____

_____

Day 3:

• What will it mean to you to have the guilt of your past deeds relieved?

_____

_____

_____

_____

_____

_____

• How would rejection and/or refusal to accept your sincere attempt at amends affect you? How about a very angry response that gets personal and insulting?

_____

_____

_____

_____

_____

_____

• What can be done about anyone that doubts your motives in making amends?

_____

_____

_____

_____

_____

_____

_____

_____

_____

• Read and slowly re-read while meditating over Romans 13:7-10

Day 4:

• The thought of doing step 9 can be anxiety-producing. The reality of not doing it can be living a life of weak and shaky sobriety. Imagine on paper the way keeping these amends to yourself might affect you.

_____

_____

_____

_____

_____

_____

_____

• How might avoiding restitution affect the way others see you as a professing Christian?

_____

_____

_____

_____

_____

_____

_____

_____

_____

_____

• Visualize the freedom of not having to be worried that you may encounter someone that you owe money or even just an apology. Describe that on paper.

_____
_____
_____
_____
_____
_____
_____
_____
_____

• Read Luke 6:37-38 and pray it settles into your heart. Measuring others as you wish to be measured seems important. Does it have any value to you?

_____
_____
_____
_____
_____
_____
_____
_____
_____
_____
_____
_____
_____
_____
_____
_____
_____

Workbook Step 10

"Continued to take personal inventory, and when we were wrong, promptly admitted it."

At the end of step 9 in the AA Big Book, there is a section called *"the promises"*. It talks about the changes that have come about as a result of working the steps honestly and without delay. By the time you get to step 10, you are probably several months out from your last use. Your life should be getting a great deal better.

Perfect? Heck no. Much better? Absolutely!

Feeling better with regard to your relationships with family, friends, and co-workers is such a great gift. Recapturing your health, improving exercise, nutrition, and sleep allow you to feel as if you have added years to your life. Becoming a regular Bible reading, church-attending, small group joining, and earnest praying Christian is a blessing that cannot be measured.

Yes, mind, body, and spirit have all benefitted greatly. Praise God! Unfortunately, life will continue to happen. Economic difficulties, social strife, devastating diagnoses all may be in your future. Life continues, and as they say, you are going to have to *"Live life on life's terms."* Steps 10, 11, and 12 are all about maintaining and improving on the progress that you have made to date.

Step 10 is about *"Them"* constantly monitoring your interactions with others and mending any missteps is a sign of a maturing Christian life. It is an important skill to learn to monitor your feelings in your body and then translate them into an understanding of what the associated thoughts are. Take this skill seriously and love *"Them"* the way God commands.

Day 1:

• Where in your body do you feel anxiety the most? Anger? Loneliness? Journal about these as you understand them now, but pay attention to them in the coming weeks to get a better understanding of yourself.

_____

_____

_____

_____

_____

_____

_____

• How do your *"wrongs"* that you may do day-to-day negatively affect you?

_____

_____

_____

_____

_____

_____

_____

• Starting tonight: take a brief inventory of your day. Ask God to convict you on any areas that you need to make right with another. Do this for the rest of your life.

• Read and meditate on 1 Corinthians 3:16. Journal on its meaning to you.

_____

_____

_____

_____

_____

_____

_____

_____

_____

_____

Day 2:

• Is there a resentment that the "*steps*" actually go on forever? Why?

_____

_____

_____

_____

_____

_____

• Do you set yourself up for resentments, by expecting others to act in a way that pleases you? How can you battle this tendency?

_____

_____

_____

_____

_____

_____

• Do you battle obsessive thinking? Has this occupied too much of your bandwidth, and should you seek professional assistance in this area?

_____

_____

_____

_____

_____

_____

• Are there things that you keep in that you should share out loud with a friend or your RP?

_____
_____
_____
_____
_____
_____
_____
_____
_____
_____

• How do you see your current state of self-care? Include mind, body, and spirit.

_____
_____
_____
_____
_____
_____
_____
_____
_____

• 1 Peter 5:6-11 has a message for you. Spend time with it and pray over it today, and then journal what it means to you.

_____
_____
_____
_____
_____
_____
_____
_____

Day 3:

• Spot inventories are different than end-of-day evaluations. Where do you see them fitting into your transformed life?

_____
_____
_____
_____
_____
_____
_____
_____

• Does the ability to understand your physical feelings and the spot inventory seem to link together well? Discuss how this may become a useful tool.

_____
_____
_____
_____
_____
_____
_____
_____
_____

• Review your Relapse Prevention Plan and see if any additions could help you in times of trouble. Finally, make a list of what you stand to lose if you don't take admitting 100% powerlessness over your addiction. Don't just skim over it; take this document seriously. It could save your life.

Today's verse: 2 John 1:8. Keep it close to your heart.

Workbook Step 11

"Sought through prayer and meditation to improve our conscious contact with our Creator, praying only for knowledge of His will for us and the power to carry it out."

"Call to me, and I will answer you, and will tell you great and hidden things that you have not known" Jeremiah 33:3

It seems almost strange to be talking about prayer and meditation as step 11. We have been instructing you to pray and meditate for months now, so it appears to be a bit after the fact to talk about it now.

Prayer is such a foundational component of Christian life that it can hardly be over-discussed. The Creator of the world put life in you for a singular reason: to have a relationship with human-you as you hopefully learn about unconditional love. He knew you before the start of time and before your birth; your assignment during your time here is to get to know Him. It is common for people to have a *"God moment"* while developing along these steps. They often say that they are having a spiritual experience. The truth is, that you aren't a human being having a spiritual experience, you have always been a spiritual being and you are currently having a human experience.

That is a game-changer.

Instead of thinking of prayer and meditation as an *"add on"* to your human life, ponder the fact that you have always had a direct line to the Creator of the Universe, but have not always used it to its fullest. It is almost like a language that you forgot at birth but can relearn at any time in your life, as soon as you desire. It is far easier than learning a new language, though, because you are already programmed to speak it.

Don't get all caught up in the flowery language that some religious people use. Jesus spent most of his ministry telling these people to knock it off. (see Mark 12:38-40) He said that their pretending they were more holy than anyone else because they followed the rules better, or held a high position in the temple, or they prayed some particular way was not only useless but worked against them. *"The first will be last and the last will be first."* It's as plain as day.

The point is, don't get all caught up in the words, but instead get caught up in actually connecting with your Heavenly Father who loves you. It's far easier than most people make it out to be.

Day 1:

• Journal about any fears that you have about contact with God.

_____

_____

_____

_____

_____

_____

_____

• Have you prayed hard for something in the past and felt your prayers went unanswered? Discuss your feelings about that.

_____

_____

_____

_____

_____

_____

_____

• Review your gratitude list and, see if you can add anything that has occurred over the last few months. Pray over each item slowly and deliberately today.

Read Matthew 6:6, and journal over it.

_____
_____
_____
_____
_____
_____
_____
_____
_____

Day 2:

• Do you have reservations about the word "*meditation*"? Write a definition as it applies to you.

_____
_____
_____
_____
_____
_____

• Look into several free apps that you can try over the next few days and see if they might become comfortable with time. List any resource which you think might help.

_____
_____
_____
_____
_____
_____

• Psalm 19:14 is waiting to speak to you. Read and journal about it.

_____

_____

_____

_____

_____

_____

_____

• So is Hebrews 4:12 do the same with it.

_____

_____

_____

_____

_____

_____

Day 3:

• Contemplative, or centering prayer is a form of Christian meditation where the person slowly reads through the word maybe a few words or sentence at a time. Google it and spend a little time investigating it.

Try it out for a time and see if it feels comfortable to you.

It is easy to find millions of people who can give you advice on exactly how to pray. Many of them mean well, but are just making up new rules. Luckily for us, Jesus had some instruction on the subject: Matthew 6:5-15, Mark 7:6-7, John 4:23-24, Journal your thoughts on these verses.

_____

_____

_____

_____

_____

Workbook Step 12

This week you will continue the lifelong process of looking for God's purpose in your life. Spend time every day for the rest of your life asking Your Heavenly Father to reveal His will for your life and for the strength to carry it out.

"Our Lord Jesus modeled many things to us on how to live our lives. Perhaps the most obvious was that of servanthood. For the Son of Man did not come to be served, but to serve and to give His life as a ransom for many." Mark 10:45

Day 1:

• What would you say your greatest strengths are?

_____

_____

_____

_____

_____

_____

_____

_____

• What are your initial thoughts for service to others, and where you might want to plug-in?

_____

_____

_____

_____

_____

_____

_____

"Each one should use whatever gifts he has received to serve others, faithfully administering God's grace in its various forms." 1 Peter 4:10

Day 2:

• Google *"volunteering near me"*. Ponder any suggestions to see where the light of God might be shown in new places. What did you find?

_____
_____
_____
_____
_____
_____
_____
_____
_____
_____

• Ask several trusted godly people for suggestions on areas of volunteerism. What did they come up with and how do you feel about those suggestions?

_____
_____
_____
_____
_____
_____
_____
_____
_____

"Work willingly at whatever you do, as though you were working for the Lord rather than for people."
Colossians 3:23

Day 3:

• Can you easily identify an area where you have a readily developed passion to serve? If so, where, and how might you expand that to include Kingdom work?

_____

_____

_____

_____

_____

_____

_____

_____

_____

_____

• Contact a pastor or minister at your church to discuss further suggestions of your particular church's needs. Discuss that conversation.

_____

_____

_____

_____

_____

_____

_____

_____

_____

_____

"Then I heard the voice of the Lord, saying,
"Whom shall I send, and who will go for Us?"
Then I said, "Here am I. Send me!" Isaiah 6:8

Relapse Prevention Plan

• Everything I can remember about my last relapse:

_____

_____

_____

_____

_____

_____

_____

_____

_____

_____

_____

_____

_____

_____

_____

_____

_____

• The one before that:

_____

_____

_____

_____

_____

_____

_____

_____

_____

_____

_____

_____

_____

My Trigger	Alternative Action
_____	_____
_____	_____
_____	_____
_____	_____
_____	_____
_____	_____
_____	_____
_____	_____
_____	_____
_____	_____
_____	_____
_____	_____

• Emotional Relapse To Me:

_____
_____
_____
_____
_____
_____
_____
_____
_____
_____
_____
_____
_____
_____
_____
_____
_____
_____
_____

• Mental Relapse to me:

_____

_____

_____

_____

_____

_____

_____

_____

_____

_____

_____

_____

_____

_____

_____

_____

_____

• Physical Relapse to me:

_____

_____

_____

_____

_____

_____

_____

_____

_____

_____

_____

_____

_____

_____

_____

_____

• What I lose if I don't take surrender seriously:

_____
_____
_____
_____
_____
_____
_____
_____
_____
_____
_____
_____
_____
_____
_____
_____
_____
_____
_____
_____
_____
_____
_____
_____
_____
_____
_____
_____
_____
_____
_____
_____
_____

Gratitude List:

Notes: